# The Sale

Written by Geri Lockington
Illustrated by Linda Costello

AVANTIBOOKS LIMITED

AVANTI
BOOKS
LIMITED

**Other titles in series:**
A Lucky Find
The Barbecue
The Garden Centre
The Little Black Cat
The Storm

ISBN: 1898614 23 7

Sally lives in a flat with her best friend Pat.

Sally has her own bedroom in the flat.

In the bedroom, Sally has her own

television and her own C.D. player.

Sally likes to sit in her room.

She likes to watch television

or put on her C.D. player.

Sally got her television in a sale.

The television was a good price.

Pat has her own room in the flat,

but she has not got her own television.

Pat wants to get her own television,

to put in her own room.

Sally and Pat went to the shop with

the sale.

They went to get a television

for Pat to put in her bedroom.

The televisions, that had been in the sale,

had all been sold.

Sally and Pat looked at lots of other televisions but they all cost a lot of money. Pat was upset.

They went back to the flat on the bus.

Pat still had her money in her bag.

At the flat was a car.

Pat's Mum was in the car.

In the back of the car was a big box.

In the box was a television.

Pat's Mum had been to the shop
with the sale.

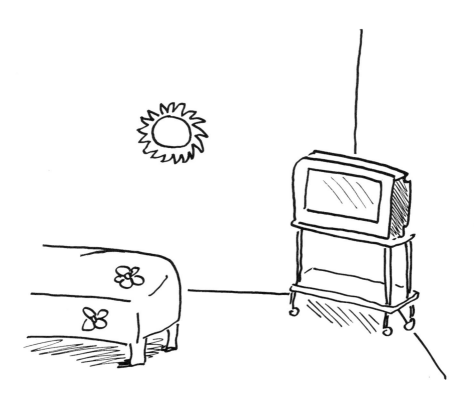

She had got the last television in the sale.

It was for Pat. Pat was pleased.

She put the television in her room in the flat.

Now she can watch her own television

in her own bedroom.